# Franz Schubert

## Symphony No. 8 in C major / C-Dur

### D944 'Great'

Edited by / Herausgegeben von
Roger Fiske

**EULENBURG**

EAS 146
ISBN 978-3-7957-6546-0
ISMN M-2002-2370-5

© 2007 Ernst Eulenburg & Co GmbH, Mainz
for Europe excluding the British Isles
Ernst Eulenburg Ltd, London
for all other countries
Edition based on Eulenburg Study Score ETP 410
CD ℗ & © 1994 Naxos Rights International Ltd

Ernst Eulenburg Ltd
48 Great Marlborough Street
London W1F 7BB

# Contents / Inhalt

# Preface

Composed: 1825/1826 in Vienna
First performance: 21 March 1839 in a Leipzig Gewandhaus concert,
conducted by Felix Mendelssohn Bartholdy
First publication: Breitkopf & Härtel, Leipzig, 1840, full score 1849
Orchestration: 2 flutes, 2 oboes, 2 clarinets, 2 bassoons – 2 horns,
2 trumpets, 3 trombones – timpani – strings
Duration: ca. 56 minutes

Although Schubert's C major Symphony is known as the 'Great', to distinguish it from a lesser predecessor in the same key, its nickname also refers to its artistic stature, as well as to what Schumann admiringly called its 'heavenly length'. Recent research has placed the composition of this masterpiece in the year 1825, whereas it was formerly thought to date from 1828, the last year of the composer's life. The reasoning behind the mistaken assumption of its being a late work is based upon its extraordinary confidence and emotional convictions, but in any case 'early' or 'late' are surely questionable attributions when an artist dies at the age of 31, with a working career of less than 20 years duration behind him.

The story of Schubert's life has been thoroughly romanticised, and an image – which has persisted almost unto the present day – of a totally instinctive creator doing what he did while scarcely knowing how or why is, of course, a serious distortion of the reality. Schubert was a man of strong character who dominated his artistic circle of writers and painters, and his music with its immense range of emotional nuance, shows him to have been an unique mixture of subtlety and forcefulness. His undoubted fluency in improvisation gave rise to that legend of untutored spontaneity beloved of romantic mythmakers which persisted throughout the 19th century and deceived even so astute a musician as Busoni, who never played Schubert in public, dismissing him as a 'rustic composer'.

As always in such cases, the truth lies between the extremes of such judgements as would make him out to be a careless creator hardly aware of the implications of his work, or the poet of a dark sensibility whose production is replete with an anguish which reflects the painful circumstances under which it came into being. There is, of course, a truth of a kind in both such views of Schubert. He seems for the most part to have been a composer whose talent permitted him to realise his music with far less overt reflection, revision or indeed preliminary sketching than, for example, his great contemporary Beethoven. For the most part his first thoughts were allowed to stand, and this insistence upon the inspiration of the moment led to an unusually large number of pieces being left incomplete, often for no obvious reason.

This strongly suggests that Schubert, unlike most other masters of his stature, really was a 'first-time' composer, in a similar way to painters like Hals or Sargent, renowned for their ability to create 'à premier coup'.

The benefit of this approach can, in all three cases, be perceived in terms of an extraordinary vitality, and such indeed is the hallmark of Schubert's music whatever its mood, however much difficulty we might have in accepting the idea that it was never produced as the result of preliminary reflection and experiment.

The 'Great' C major Symphony was preceded by no less than three incomplete symphonies, one of which, always known as the 'Unfinished', is almost his best-known work. The 'Great' is at the opposite pole of expression to his sombrely reflective B minor Symphony. It is ebullient, confident, almost grandiose in manner, a tremendous celebration of the life-force itself. At first its vast scale and unusually repetitive style caused problems for its earliest performers, but, like the Ninth Symphony of Beethoven, which Schubert almost certainly heard the year before at its premiere, it sets a new standard for an expansion of musical expression which continued throughout the 19th century and well into the 20th.

Despite its optimistic and at times almost manic vitality, there are, as there must be in any work of genuine achievement, a whole range of expressive options. Even the opening, a mysterious and emotionally ambiguous introduction, half heroic, half melancholic, and leading imperceptibly into a vigorous *Allegro*, already suggests a whole new vision of musical reality. Such transformations, where the familiar is constantly modified to yield new experiences, are achieved by a subtle integration of melodic elements; one of Schubert's most significant contributions to Western musical language lies in his fascination with the re-appearance of melodic fragments in new contexts. In a sense, this is a kind of long-term variation technique, and accounts in part for the greatly expanded time-scale of Schubert's mature works. The 19th century made great use of this discovery, and Liszt, himself a pioneer of the technique of thematic transformation, made a special study of Schubert's music culminating in his transcription of the Wanderer-Fantasy for piano and orchestra.

The 'Great' C major Symphony remained unperformed in public until Mendelssohn conducted its first complete performance in 1839; the music caused serious problems, both technical and conceptual, to its earliest players. Full acceptance of the work by the public was delayed until the latter part of the 19th century, by which time music on such a similarly expansive scale was beginning to seem more acceptable. Its influence on composers was, however, much more immediate and complete: almost the only element shared by the Leipzig school of Mendelssohn and Schumann with their firm opponents, the New German movement of Wagner and Liszt, was their conviction of Schubert's artistic stature and historical importance. Bruckner too, whose own music had its roots in an earlier classicism, was deeply influenced by the 'Great' C major; its expanded form and elevated diction matching his own enthusiasm for a music of philosophical reflection and monumental structure.

Although it is difficult to imagine Schubert's having been able to achieve the 'Great' C major without the example of Beethoven's Ninth before him – and indeed he himself advertised the connection by direct quotation in the Finale – nevertheless the only real element they share is a vastly expanded sense of scale: their expressive concerns are entirely different. Where Beethoven explores the ideal of the brotherhood of man, Schubert celebrates the power of nature, man's place in the natural world, and its influence on his psychological and spiritual development. The 'Great' C major Symphony, in its power and amplitude, represents the fullest statement of Schubert's philosophical position: a view of nature as a mysterious force, independent of man, but with which he finds it imperative to engage, in order to know himself more fully.

Justin Connolly

Our numbering of the Schubert symphonies follows that of the New Schubert Edition (*Franz Schubert: Neue Ausgabe sämtlicher Werke*) and the Deutsch Schubert Catalogue (*Franz Schubert: Thematisches Verzeichnis seiner Werke, von Otto Erich Deutsch*). The 'Unfinished' Symphony (D759), formerly listed as No. 8, is therefore renumbered No. 7; the 'Great' (D944), formerly listed as No. 9, is therefore renumbered as No. 8.

# Vorwort

**Komponiert: 1825/1826 in Wien**
**Uraufführung: 21. März 1839 in einem Konzert des Leipziger**
**Gewandhauses unter der Leitung von Felix Mendelssohn Bartholdy**
**Originalverlag: Breitkopf & Härtel, Leipzig, 1840, Partitur 1849**
**Orchesterbesetzung: 2 Flöten, 2 Oboen, 2 Klarinetten, 2 Fagotte –**
**2 Hörner, 2 Trompeten, 3 Posaunen – Pauken – Streicher**
**Spieldauer: etwa 56 Minuten**

Schuberts Symphonie in C-Dur wird zwar die ,Große' genannt, um sie von einer kleineren Vorgängerin in derselben Tonart zu unterscheiden, doch bezieht sich ihr Beiname auch auf ihren künstlerischen Rang sowie auf das, was Schumann bewundernd ihre ,himmlische Länge' nannte. Jüngste Untersuchungen haben die Komposition dieses Meisterwerks ins Jahr 1825 verlegt, während man früher meinte, es datiere von 1828, dem letzten Lebensjahr des Komponisten. Das Argument für die irrtümliche Annahme, dass es ein Spätwerk sei, besteht in seiner außerordentlichen Kühnheit und emotionalen Gewalt. Auf jeden Fall aber sind ,früh' oder ,spät' gewiss fragwürdige Zuordnungen, wenn ein Künstler schon im Alter von 31 Jahren, nach einer Schaffenslaufbahn von weniger als 20 Jahren, stirbt.

Schuberts Lebensgeschichte ist durchweg romantisiert worden, und das Bild, das fast bis auf den heutigen Tag überdauert hat – das Bild von einem ganz und gar instinktiven Schöpfer, der kaum weiß, wie und warum er tut, was er tut –, ist natürlich eine gröbliche Verzerrung der Wirklichkeit. Schubert war ein Mann von starkem Charakter, der in seinem Künstlerkreis von Schriftstellern und Malern der *primus inter pares* war, und seine Musik mit dem immensen Reichtum ihrer Gefühlsabstufungen zeigt, dass er ein einzigartiges Amalgam aus Kraft und Subtilität gewesen ist. Seine unbestrittene Geläufigkeit im Improvisieren ließ die Legende von einer naiven Spontaneität aufkommen, wie sie romantische Mythenbildner liebten – eine Legende, die sich das ganze 19. Jahrhundert hindurch hielt und selbst einen so scharfsinnigen Musiker wie Busoni täuschte, der in der Öffentlichkeit nie Schubert spielte, da er diesen als einen ,bäurischen Komponisten' abtat.

Wie immer in solchen Fällen liegt die Wahrheit zwischen den Extremen solcher Urteile: Schubert als unbekümmerter Schöpfer, der sich der Implikationen seines Werkes kaum bewusst gewesen sei, einerseits, als Tondichter einer dunklen Empfindsamkeit, dessen Produktion gesättigt sei von einem Leide, das die schmerzensreichen Umstände ihrer Genese widerspiegele, andererseits. In beiden dieser Ansichten über Schubert steckt natürlich ein Körnchen Wahrheit. Er scheint meistenteils ein Komponist gewesen zu sein, dessen Talent ihm gestattete, seine Musik mit viel weniger offenkundiger Reflexion, Überarbeitung oder gar vorausgehender Skizzenarbeit zu verwirklichen als zum Beispiel sein großer Zeitgenosse Beethoven. Meist durften seine ersten Einfälle stehen bleiben, und sein Beharren auf der Inspiration des Augenblicks führte zu einer ungewöhnlich großen Anzahl von Stücken, die – oft aus keinem einsichtigen Grund – unvollendet blieben. Dies legt den zwingenden Gedanken nahe, dass Schubert, ungleich den meisten anderen Meistern seines Ranges, tatsächlich ein Komponist des ‚beim ersten Mal‘ war, nicht unähnlich den Malern Frans Hals oder John Singer Sargent, die für ihre Fähigkeit berühmt waren, Werke *à premier coup* zu erschaffen.

Der Vorzug dieser Herangehensweise kann in allen drei Fällen im Sinne einer außerordentlichen Vitalität gesehen werden, und diese ist denn auch in der Tat das Kennzeichen von Schuberts Musik, wie immer sie just gestimmt ist und wie schwer es uns auch fallen mag, die Vorstellung zu akzeptieren, dass sie nie als Resultat eines vorausgehenden Reflektierens und Experimentierens erschaffen wurde.

Der ‚großen‘ C-Dur-Symphonie gingen nicht weniger als drei fragmentarische Symphonien voraus, von denen eine, die stets die ‚Unvollendete‘ genannt wird, sein nachgerade bekanntestes Werk ist. Zu dieser düster-schwersinnigen h-Moll-Sinfonie nimmt die ‚Große‘ auf der Skala des Ausdrucks den Gegenpol ein. Sie ist überschwänglich, optimistisch, geradezu grandios im Ton, eine gewaltige Verherrlichung von Lebenskraft selbst. Ihre riesigen Dimensionen und ihr ungewöhnlich repetitiver Stil bereiteten ihren ersten Interpreten zunächst Probleme, doch gleich der neunten Symphonie Beethovens, deren Uraufführung Schubert fast sicher im Jahre zuvor gehört hatte, setzte sie einen neuen Standard für eine Erweiterung des musikalischen Ausdrucks, der sich durch das ganze 19. Jahrhundert bis weit ins 20. hinein behauptete.

Trotz seiner optimistischen, mitunter fast manischen Vitalität gibt es in diesem Werk – wie es in Werken solcher Vollendung gar nicht anders sein kann – ein ganzes Spektrum expressiver Optionen. Schon der Beginn, eine mysteriöse und emotional ambivalente Introduktion, halb heroisch, halb melancholisch und unmerklich in ein energisches *Allegro ma non troppo* geleitend, verweist bereits auf eine gänzlich neue Vision von musikalischer Wirklichkeit. Solche Transformationen, in denen das Vertraute beständig abgewandelt wird, um neuen Erfahrungen Raum zu geben, werden durch eine subtile Integration melodischer Elemente erreicht; einer der bedeutendsten Beiträge Schuberts zur Musiksprache des Abendlands beruht auf seiner Faszination vom Wiedererscheinen melodischer Fragmente in neuen Kontexten. In gewissem Sinne ist dies eine Art Variationstechnik in erweitertem Maßstab, aus der sich zum Teil die erhebliche zeitliche Dimensionierung der reifen Werke Schuberts erklärt. Das 19. Jahrhundert zog großen Nutzen aus dieser Entdeckung, und Liszt, der selber in der Technik thematischer Verwandlung ein Pionier war, nahm sich, etwa in seiner h-Moll-Sonate, insbesondere Schuberts Musik zum Modell, was in seiner Transkription der Wanderer-Phantasie für Klavier und Orchester kulminierte.

Die ‚große‘ C-Dur-Symphonie blieb der Öffentlichkeit verschlossen, bis Mendelssohn ihre erste vollständige Aufführung 1839 im Leipziger Gewandhaus dirigierte. Die Musik konfrontierte ihre ersten Ausführenden mit beträchtlichen Schwierigkeiten sowohl technischer wie konzeptioneller Art. Die volle Akzeptanz des Werkes durch die Öffentlichkeit verzögerte sich bis ins späte 19. Jahrhundert. Erst dann, wie es scheint, begann Musik von solch vergleichsweise expansiven Dimensionen eher akzeptiert zu werden. Ihr Einfluss auf Komponisten war jedoch weit unmittelbarer und umfassender: Nahezu das einzige, was die Leipziger Schule Mendelssohns und Schumanns mit ihren entschiedenen Gegnern, den ‚Neudeutschen' um Wagner und Liszt, gemeinsam hatte, war ihre Überzeugung von Schuberts künstlerischem Rang und seiner historischen Bedeutung. Auch Bruckner, dessen eigene Musik in einem älteren Klassizismus wurzelte, wurde von der ‚großen' C-Dur-Symphonie tief beeinflusst. Ihre erweiterte Form und elevierte Tonsprache trafen sich mit seiner eigenen Begeisterung für eine Musik der philosophischen Reflexion und der monumentalen Architektonik.

Mag es auch schwer fallen sich vorzustellen, Schubert hätte die ‚Große' in C-Dur ohne das Vorbild von Beethovens Neunter konzipieren können – er selbst offenbart ja den Einfluss durch direktes Zitieren des ‚Freuden-Themas' in seinem Finale (*Allegro vivace*) –, so ist nichtsdestoweniger das einzige, was die beiden Komponisten wirklich gemeinsam haben, ein Sinn für gewaltig erweiterte Dimensionen. Ihre Ausdrucksbestrebungen sind völlig verschieden. Während Beethoven das Ideal einer Menschheitsverbrüderung auslotet, verherrlicht Schubert die Kraft der Natur, den Platz des Menschen in der Ordnung der Natur und ihren Einfluss auf seine seelische und geistige Entfaltung. Die ‚große' C-Dur-Symphonie repräsentiert in ihrer Kraft und in ihrem Gestaltenreichtum die vollkommenste Darlegung von Schuberts philosophischer Haltung: eine Sicht von Natur als einer geheimnisvollen Kraft, geschieden vom Menschen, der sich doch aufgerufen fühlt, sich mit ihr zu vereinen, um sich selbst tiefer zu verstehen.

Justin Connolly


Unsere Nummerierung der Schubert-Symphonien folgt derjenigen in der Neuen Schubert-Ausgabe (*Franz Schubert: Neue Ausgabe sämtlicher Werke*) sowie in Deutschs Werkverzeichnis (*Franz Schubert: Thematisches Verzeichnis seiner Werke, von Otto Erich Deutsch*). Demnach wird die ‚Unvollendete' Sinfonie (D 759), bisher Nr. 8, jetzt als Nr. 7 gezählt und die ‚Große' (D 944), bisher Nr. 9, nunmehr als Nr. 8.

# Symphony No. 8

Franz Schubert
(1797–1828)
D944

**I.** **Andante**

© 2007 Ernst Eulenburg Ltd, London
and Ernst Eulenburg & Co GmbH, Mainz

6

10

Allegro ma non troppo

EAS 146

12

EAS 146

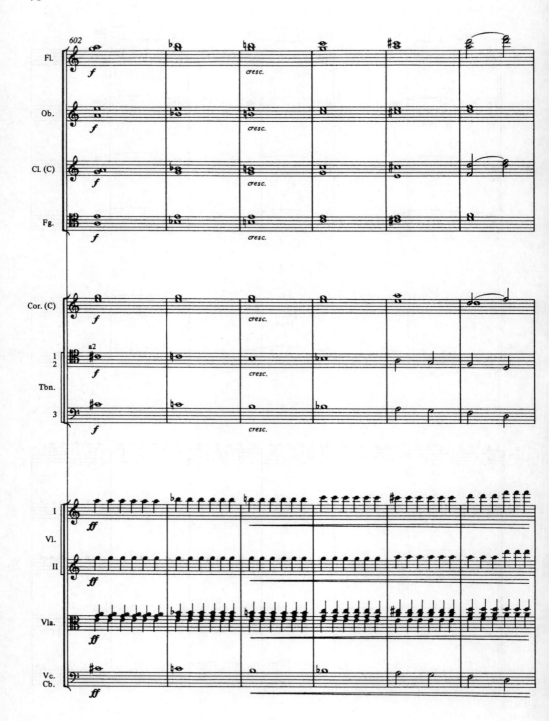

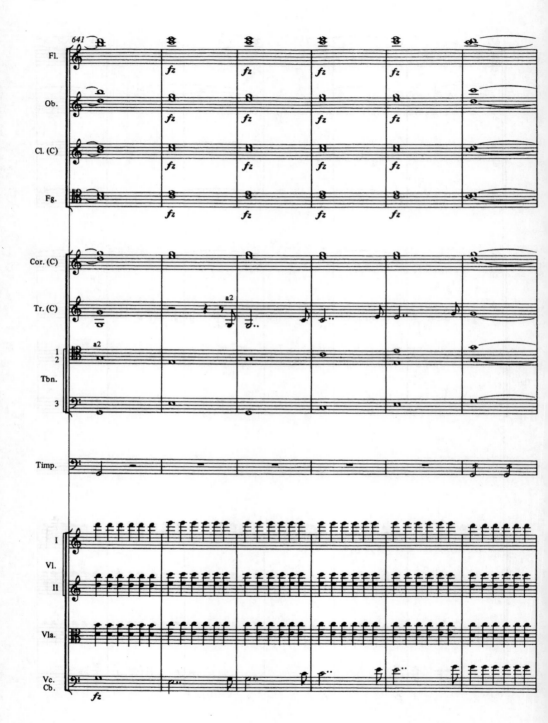

# II. Andante con moto

92

EAS 146

94

EAS 146

106

EAS 146

116

EAS 146

124

# III. Scherzo
**Allegro vivace**

EAS 146

# Trio

*Scherzo D.C. al Fine*

# IV. Finale

**Allegro vivace**

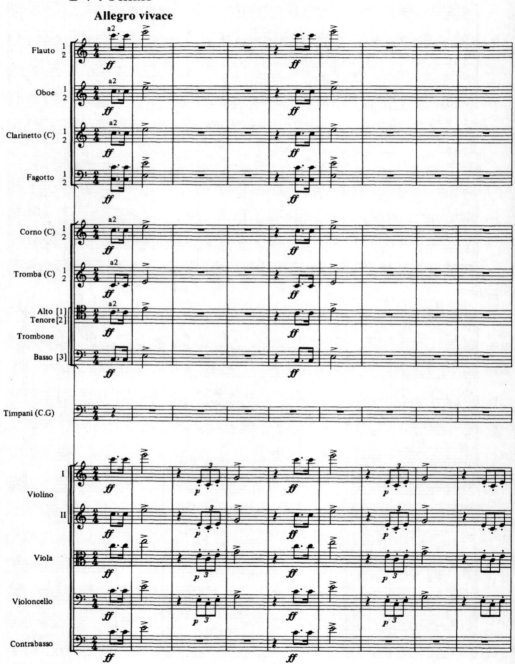

174

EAS 146

180

EAS 146

EAS 146

209

EAS 146

EAS 146

218

EAS 146

220

EAS 146

234

246

262

EAS 146

Printed in China